SALTAIRE
a PICTURE
STORYBOOK

by Simon Palmer

Dedicated to Tink, Ilona and Tamsin

It is important to thank Jonathan Silver, Ray Shilling, Linda Wilkinson and Anna Hornby who have made this book a reality as well as a dream

INTRODUCTION

**TITUS SALT REASSURES A DELEGATION
OF CONCERNED WEST RIDING FARMERS**

Farmers had heard of strange beasts at Crow Nest,
and felt it prudent
to have the affair addressed.
So Titus reassured the hill farmers
their fields would not
be taken over by Llamas.
He said they wouldn't be found grazing the heather
because Alpacas
could not stand the English weather.
So hills and valleys the farmers could keep
for producing wool
from tried and tested sheep.
To buying the fleece Titus had to resort
and of his strange flock
he had sadly to export.

Titus explained to the men of the llama story,
and how it had led
to Saltaire's fame and glory.
He spoke to them of his Liverpool trip,
and of a strange cargo
dropped by a Peruvian ship,
which was a huge pile of woollen fleece
but was black with dirt
and coated in layers of grease.

Later, he returned to the Liverpool dock
and re-examined
the pile of unwanted stock.
With a sample in hand he went back home,
where he washed, cleaned
and teased it long with a comb.

He scoured, carded and combed these new strands
alone in a room,
spinning it with his own bare hands.
After much hard work a lustrous thread was achieved
from that dirty fleece
in which Titus alone had believed.

He invited John Hammond in on the scheme;
problems could be halved
with friends working as a team.
He wanted to share his exciting find
but John was cautious
and in the end declined.
So Titus embarked on the scheme alone.
He would either swim
or go down like a stone.

Titus went back to the docks and brokers found.
Then offered to buy
the bales for eight pence a pound.
To find a purchaser they were relieved.
The brokers gladly
accepted the offer received.

To most people
Titus' vision had been a mystery,
but as in the cliché
the rest is now history.
And humble Titus reminded the farmers.
That Saltaire's success
was all down to the llamas.

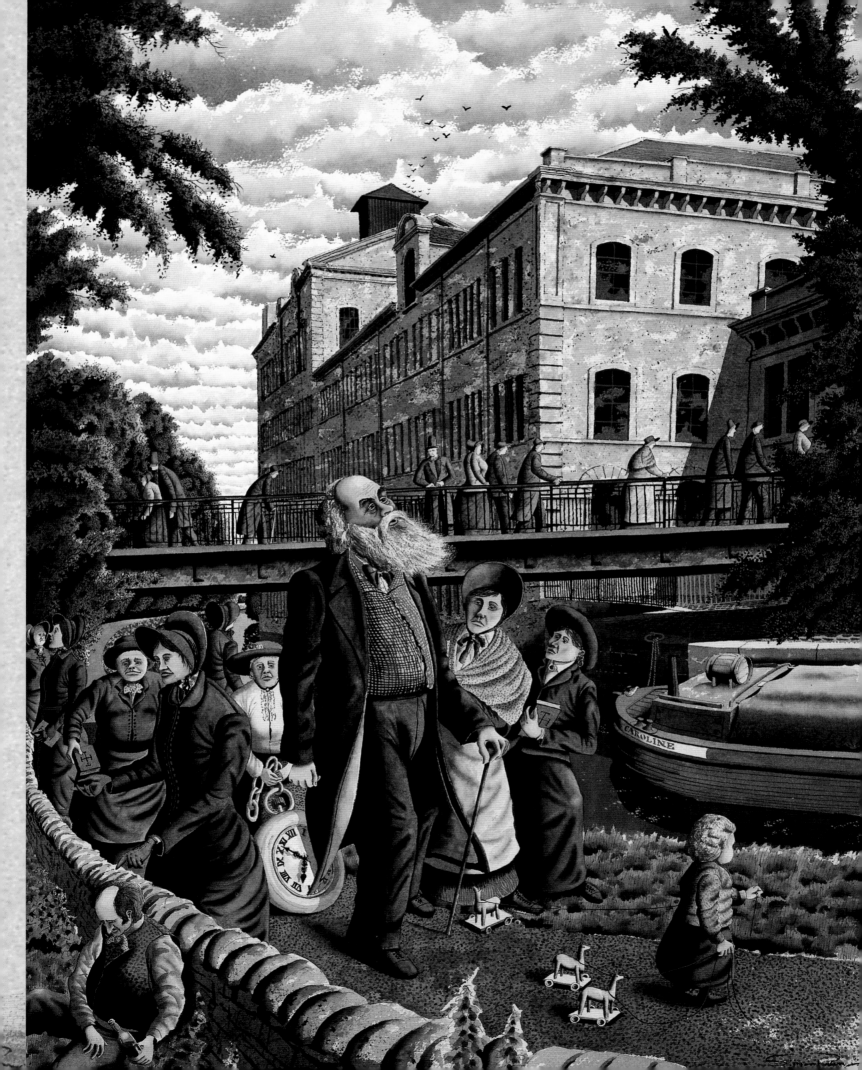

A MEDICAL REPORT TO THE IMPERIAL COMMISSION

Enclosed within is a summary of my report.
There seem to be few problems, it has my full support.

You see how it has been developed in ordered stages.
There is high class work and people are paid good wages.

Everything in the mill, of course, is top quality.
Among the huge workforce there is no frivolity.

Then there are the comfortable houses provided
between well-drained yards and gardens they are divided.

These places are tastefully decorated inside
where the honest, working, homemaking people reside.

It is medical folk like me (who are in the know)
will tell you this cleanliness helps peoples stature grow.

Good domestic conditions prevent vice and disease
with stringent efforts to stamp out mice, lice and the fleas.

Now I quickly move from work and home to leisure
which proved interesting and gave me the most pleasure.

Many folk have bought musical instruments to learn.
I was entertained five hours as they took it in turn.

The list is varied, violins, cornets, double bass;
one player made his trumpet its own llama skin case.

Activities for the skilled worker in leisure hours
taxidermy, sport and crafts or arranging flowers.

Or for those with an intelligent technical mind
let me reveal what they do after a hard days grind.

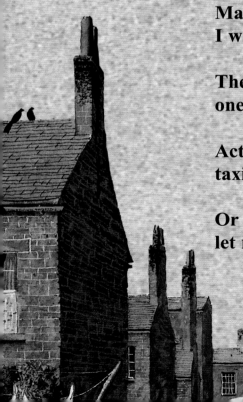

Philosophical instruments, models and air pumps;
one chap has made furniture out of local tree stumps.

There's a model steam engine top end of Wendy Street
and next door a hot air balloon made out of a sheet.

Of course numerous choral societies exist.
I'm forced to sit and listen to them all, they insist!

No public houses so there's no serious drinking.
They all stay at home absorbed in religious thinking.

There have been brand new bath and wash houses erected
and a variety of soaps have been selected.

FOOTNOTE

But between you and me,
I think you will agree,
visiting last Friday,
it's all a bit
too neat and tidy.

I found on my touring,
it's all a touch boring
and just so very nice,
without a pinch
of old fashioned vice.

Nobody getting that tight
on a Saturday night.
No punch-ups in the street,
bare fisty cuffs
thrown in for a treat.

No pretty girls to touch
and be charged far too much,
but please don't get me wrong,
I like knitting
and list'ning to song.

Getting the balance right:
some Church, the odd fight,
a session in the pub,
then sleep it off
with friends at the club.

We can't always be good.
Sometimes misunderstood,
I've been accused of libel,
but always try
and read my Bible.

THE CONGREGATIONAL CHURCH

I telephoned Mr Broomhead
(a trustee and stalwart member)
to make notes of what he said
and ask what he could remember.

So then I could collect the facts
to draw in words for simple rhyme.
With kind help from Saltaire contacts
I was transported back in time.

It's like a spiritual bond
gleaned from Salts Mill books and research,
to find that I had become fond
of the congregational church.
This ornate edifice so grand
in the northern town of Saltaire
by an industrialist planned
with philanthropy that is rare.

It "stands like a palace for God" said Sir Titus Salt
Built in the Italianate design to a fault
and a fine "place of worship for the working classes."
But for the mill
of all the buildings it surpasses,
started in fifty-eight and finished one year later
for singing praises and worshipping our creator.

THE LIONS OF SALTAIRE

They did not get the call
because they were too small.
So if their high pitched roar
is sounding somewhat poor,
or if they're in a huff
it's because they were
just not big enough.

The lions of Saltaire
really do not care.
They don't feel rejected
that they weren't selected
and that it was unfair
they were not chosen
for Trafalgar Square.

That hot polluted place
with hindsight they couldn't face.
Roundabout Trafalgar
seems terribly vulgar.
Saltaire is where they rest
so it really seems
it's turned out for the best.

Firstly comes vigilance,
so why not diligence?
Opposite peace and war
which one's licking its paw?
And then determination,
all Mister T Milne's
very own creation.

The lions west and east
each one a handsome beast
guarding the institute
where members would recruit
to play games and sport,
sign up for lectures
and expect to be taught.

The other lions showed
'cross Victoria Road
they would protect the school
though no need as a rule
due to its location,
to Titus and his
spiritual vocation.

A clean modern village
without rape and pillage.
Building churches not pubs
and education clubs.
Titus and his visions
for better homes
and working conditions.

THE SCHOOL POEM

There was a Saltaire schoolgirl,
by the name of Betty Palmer
who spent time befriending
a South American llama.

But one Tuesday it had the cheek,
to follow her into school,
which made the earnest pupil,
feel a bit of a fool.

And then when it followed Betty,
right through into class,
the morning assembly,
deteriorated into farce.

The old school chaplain intervened,
in time to give his views,
It was agreed that Titus Salt,
should be told the news.

Because of the chaos, when he arrived,
he had to shout,
and he was not in a good mood,
on account of his gout.

"Now then, what's this all about,
a school-going llama?
To drag me from the mill,
I trust it's a major drama."

When the noise had abated,
Salt asked to see young Palmer.
He stood by the teacher's blackboard,
and summoned the llama.

"I've hidden my friend" Betty said,
Standing on Titus' feet,
"I do not want it sent off,
To be cut up into meat."

"Alpacas aren't kept to be fattened,"
Titus Salt replied
"They are reared for their fine wool,
we have recently tried."

"Whatever your story,
and however you brought it here,
the llama's going back to Crow Nest.
Do I make myself clear?"

"Headmaster, I trust you can arrange
a suitable plan?
I'm a very busy man
so be as quick as you can."

"Now then, young Betty and I
are going to have a chat,
if she wants a real pet
perhaps I could find her a cat."

But as the school were in a group,
discussing this and that,
the llama strolled out of the school,
turned around its head and spat.

A LESSON ON THE LAH'-MUH

HEADMASTER'S NOTES

As long as we don't have a repeat of last weeks drama,
I thought we could have a group lesson all about the llama.

It is related to the camelidae but lacks a hump,
with long legs and neck, its tail though, is little more than a stump.

It resembles a sheep and does not differ much from a goat
and its greatest asset is in the silkiness of its coat.

But the lusty llama measures just four feet at the shoulder,
yet able to walk miles 'cross rugged terrain, strewn with boulders.

They can carry up to a hundred pound packs strapped to their backs,
across tablelands, rough plateaux and up high altitude tracks.

Domesticated by the Incas it's a useful creature
and the alpaca wool must be its most redeeming feature.

But if upset can turn stubborn and go into a sulk,
when it decides it will no longer carry its owner's bulk.

It will simply lie down and absolutely refuse to budge.
Be warned it is most unwise to prod it, or give it a nudge.
It will be your great misfortune if it harbours you a grudge.

So avoid irritating it or whacking it with a stick.
It might leap up unexpected and attack you with a kick.
But I must tell you this, it has another malicious trick
it can bring up its undigested food and spray you in sick.

A MEMORABLE CRICKET MATCH

Two days before an important cricket match was due,
half the workforce of Saltaire went down with the 'flu.
It was hard work finding a team quite right for the day.
The captain was begging retired clothworkers and sorters to play.
Desperate for an eleventh man they would have to ask
that verse monger John Nicholson to fulfil the task.

As the opposition arrived
by local steam train
Saltaire's proxy cricket team hoped
it would start to rain.
Nerves cracked up as they approached the
start at two o'clock.
The opposition's pedigree
was of fighting stock,
and an established team from the
rough end of Bradford.
With them came their notorious
bowler Don Radford.

Fearful Saltaire went into bat
like lambs to the slaughter.
Their umpire cried
"I'm just an overlooker's daughter,
my father should be umpiring
this one sided game.
It will be a real fiasco
and I'll get the blame".

Their best two batsmen were clean bowled.
The next three were caught.
It was only two fifteen and
they were five for naught.
Tho' dejected they staggered on
for the next half hour
when play was interrupted by
a welcome shower.

When play restarted Saltaire were
just twelve runs for nine.
Radford had introduced his own
style of bodyline.
The players in the changing room
accepted defeat,
ruling out miracles to win
they would have to cheat.

Picture if you can
the late arrival of Saltaire's
brave eleventh man.

He came out of the dressing room singing as he walked.
You could tell he was rolling drunk by the way he talked.
The sort of poet the captain could gladly throttle.
No bat in hand Nicholson walked out with a bottle
and when the opposition helped poet to wicket
it was obvious J N had never played cricket.
The first ball he punched for a single with his fist
and the next twenty-three long hops he completely missed.

But to anyone watching
it was perfectly clear
John the alcoholic poet
showed no signs of fear
(courage gained by too much beer).
The umpire walked over to him
and in his ear hissed
"It really is disgusting
you're absolutely ...."

But when a Radford bodyline
struck him on the back
Nicholson saw double red and
went on the attack.
He belted a sixer right
across the river Aire
which so dumbfounded the captain
he fell off his chair.
Another colossal six came
that topped Baildon Moor,
rescuing the team from rather
a pathetic score.

This fast bowler the poet was
determined to beat
and went about hitting his third
six into George Street.
But the next almighty wallop,
which outshone the rest,
the ball sent soared ten miles and bounced off the roof of Crow Nest.

But fame was short lived when he was
caught on the boundary
by a twenty-one stone bloke who
worked in a foundry.

The poet
walked up to Radford
and gave him a look.
"You can keep this cricket bat,
I'll swap it for a book.
There's one more thing
I'll say to you
and that is
I think
it is about bloody time
I had
another drink!"

GRAFFITI ON NICHOLSON

He neglected wife and their little mites
because he thought he could reach greater heights.
As poet of Airedale he set his sights.

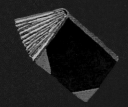

Titus Salt tolerated his drinking
to encourage John's poetical thinking.

Life for Martha and bairns was very hard
coping with this irritating Airedale bard.

John was never poet laureate crowned
he slipped into the river Aire and drowned.

I think John Nicholson must have been drunk
because when he fell into the Aire he sunk.

J N must have been forgiven his ways
because at the end of one of the hottest days

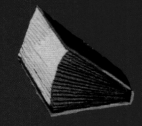

the old poet ascended into Heaven
at exactly twelve minutes past seven.

(Strongly influenced by 'Poetry Or Bust' by Tony Harrison)

HYMN (Seasonal)

We sing praises for the wondrous heatwave
And bless the washing-up water that we save
Remembering how the plants we almost lost
Punished and blackened by last April's frost
Although now we have given thanks enough
The garden is concrete
The garden's looking rough

(Chorus)
We wonder at the high temperatures last new year
The reason for blizzards in July is not clear
We question why hurricanes hit this November
You created four seasons, we must remember
Though now we've taken over and are reforming
By introducing a touch of global warming

The trees are turning a premature brown
Please we ask for some rain to be sent down
Our faith can sing through days of sorrow
Let's dance so it chucks it down tomorrow
But we must remember not to complain
When we're rewarded
With six months solid rain

We have taken our weather for granted
But saddened by dead trees that we planted
Start thinking about finding the reasons
For this abnormal change in our seasons
We will have to carry the guilty can
Before the lifting
Of this year's hosepipe ban

A PAINTING FOR SIR TITUS SALT (BART)

AN UNPUBLISHED LETTER SENT TO A LOCAL NEWSPAPER

You do not want to believe everything that you read in the papers.
The editor removed all the references to back room capers.
The outrageous antics that were stopped from going to press.
The scandal on "Medication for organisers who suffered stress".
For further information contact 'disgusted' at this address.
It began with the committee organising their first meeting;
the arguments over who should be invited took some beating,
quickly followed by an organised rumpus all about seating
and some of the deplorable language does not bear repeating.
But when they came to discuss the painting of Titus (Bart)
they fell totally silent and did not know where to start.

Nearly two thousand three hundred subscribers gave a donation.
Enough funds for a fine picture to mark the occasion;
to hang proud in the institute on the upstairs landing.
A grand portrait of Titus Salt in his office standing.
The work executed by an artist called J. P. Knight.
With wholesome credentials from the RA the choice was right.
So not procuring the commission has increased our plight.

I am the local Saltaire artist and should have done the picture.
Its not sour grapes, the painting is fine, we submit no stricture.
My work must be too modern for the town, perhaps a little abstract.
It's just our life would have been easier had I won the contract.
It appears the committee aren't prepared for today's avant garde.
Being overlooked for the commission has made life rather hard.
The way I have been rejected has made my wife most annoyed;
so much so she has had my entire portfolio destroyed.

We have started to eat the furniture and are living in rags;
sadly the youngest spent the last ha'pence on a packet of fags.
We need the money to live; it was not to indulge on treats;
just to buy a pair of shoes to share and keep us off the streets.
Yes, this is a begging letter you have now probably perceived,
so any cash, cheques or credit card will gratefully be received.

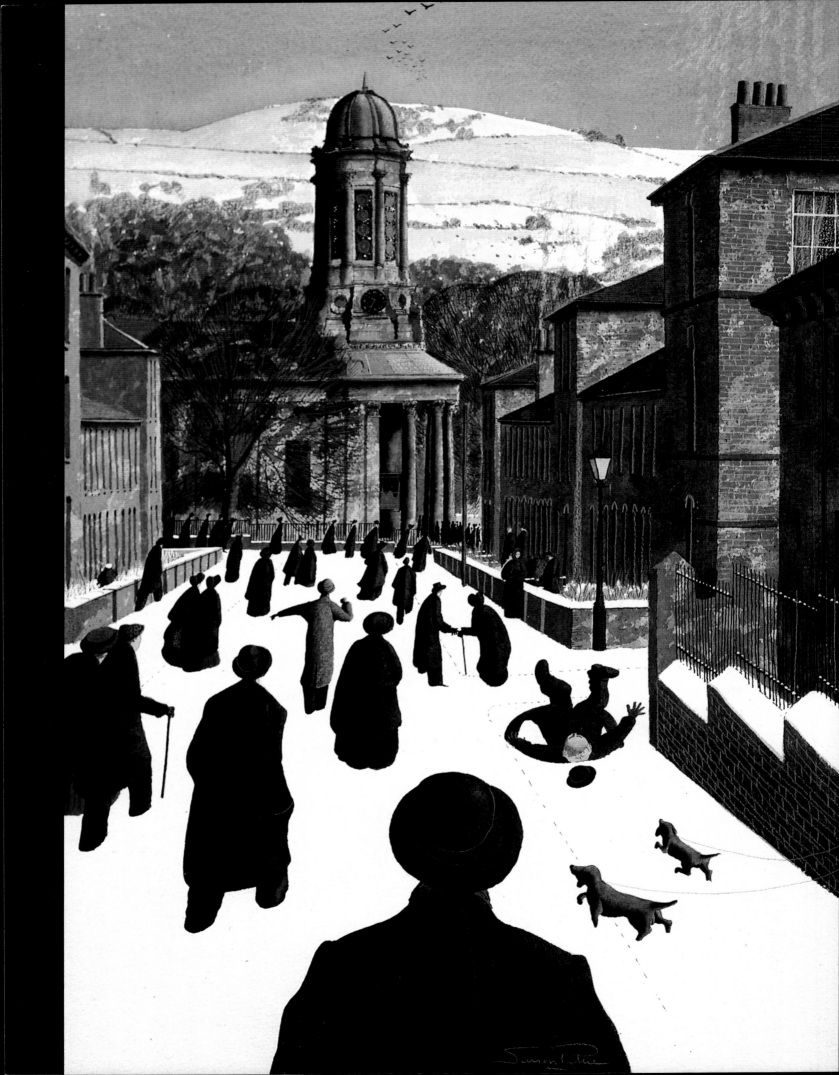

SAD NEWS

Have you not seen all the queues of people wanting the news? You must have seen the papers, queues for black at the drapers Don't tell me you have not read the news, Sir Titus Salt is dead.

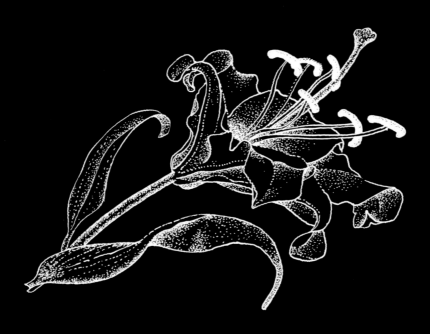

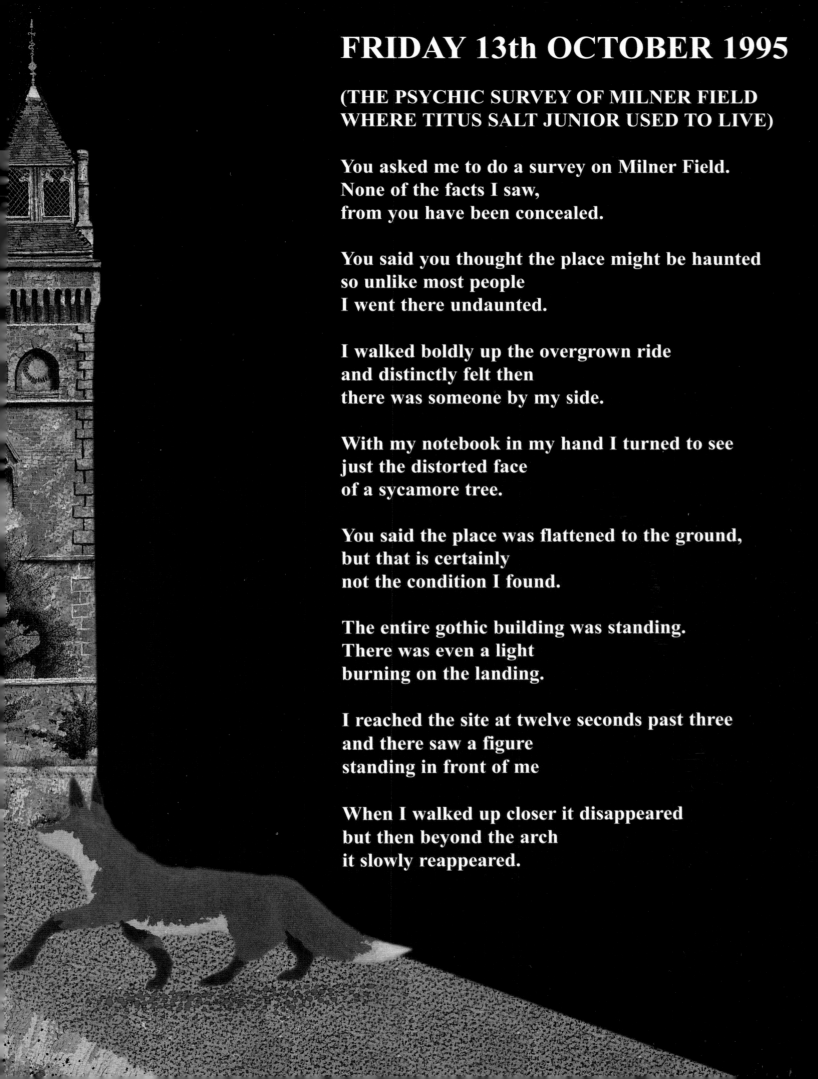

FRIDAY 13th OCTOBER 1995

**(THE PSYCHIC SURVEY OF MILNER FIELD
WHERE TITUS SALT JUNIOR USED TO LIVE)**

You asked me to do a survey on Milner Field.
None of the facts I saw,
from you have been concealed.

You said you thought the place might be haunted
so unlike most people
I went there undaunted.

I walked boldly up the overgrown ride
and distinctly felt then
there was someone by my side.

With my notebook in my hand I turned to see
just the distorted face
of a sycamore tree.

You said the place was flattened to the ground,
but that is certainly
not the condition I found.

The entire gothic building was standing.
There was even a light
burning on the landing.

I reached the site at twelve seconds past three
and there saw a figure
standing in front of me

When I walked up closer it disappeared
but then beyond the arch
it slowly reappeared.

It wore tail coat, gloves and classic top hat
and was Titus Junior.
I am quite sure of that.

I saw a ghostly hearse in that moonlight.
That strange phenomenon
was a disturbing sight.

When I heard the hall organ being played,
to you a confession :
I was growing afraid.

It was more a nightmare than psychic dream
when from the upstairs landing
a girl began to scream.

From the south terrace the hearse returned
when it stopped at my side
my knotted stomach churned.

Stepping from the coach it was plain to see
three pale undertakers
were coming for me.

But before they touched, they melted away,
off into the darkness
before the dawn of next day.

When I decided it was time to leave
someone in a tailcoat
grabbed me by the sleeve.

Sir Titus Salt looked at me and said
"This is a doomed place;
that is what I have read.
Milner Field is not for the living,
but for the dead".